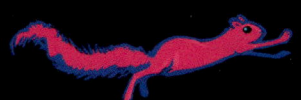

GENIUS ANIMALS?

by

Vali Chandrasekaran
&
Jun-Pierre Shiozawa

SHIOZAWA

COLD FUSION
INDUSTRIES

Published by Cold Fusion Industries
All Rights Reserved

Library of Congress Control Number: 2021918814

Paperback ISBN: 978-1-34388-373-4

For all inquiries please contact
Cold Fusion Industries by email at geniusanimals@gmail.com

First edition, 2021
printed in South Korea

Edited by Vali Chandrasekaran
Designed by Jun-Pierre Shiozawa

COLD FUSION
INDUSTRIES

CHAPTER 1

TWO JAMESONS PLEASE.

WHAT'S HIS DEAL?

HE'S IN A PARODY BAND.

OUR BAND NAME IS "BAND NAME."

I'M SORRY.

THAT GUY SMELLS LIKE AN OLD BAG OF SPINACH.

clink!

LOOK, IT'S 11:00. WE COULD LEAVE BUT THEN WE'D JUST GO HOME.

ARE YOU ABOUT TO START SOME SORT OF "YEAR OF SAYING 'YES'" THING? IF SO, I'M GOING TO ASK YOU TO MOVE OUT.

FIRST OF ALL, THEME YEARS GET A BAD RAP. THERE'S SOME EVIDENCE *LINCOLN* WAS IN THE MIDDLE OF A "YEAR OF SAYING 'YES'" WHEN HE FREED THE SLAVES.

SECOND, THAT'S *NOT* WHAT I'M DOING. WORK HAS BEEN STRESSFUL LATELY. SO I REALLY WANT TO HAVE A GOOD TIME TONIGHT.

HOW?

JUST A WARNING. I'M AT THE END OF MY LAUNDRY CYCLE.

I'M *ALEXANDRA* BY THE WAY.

I'M *TODD.*

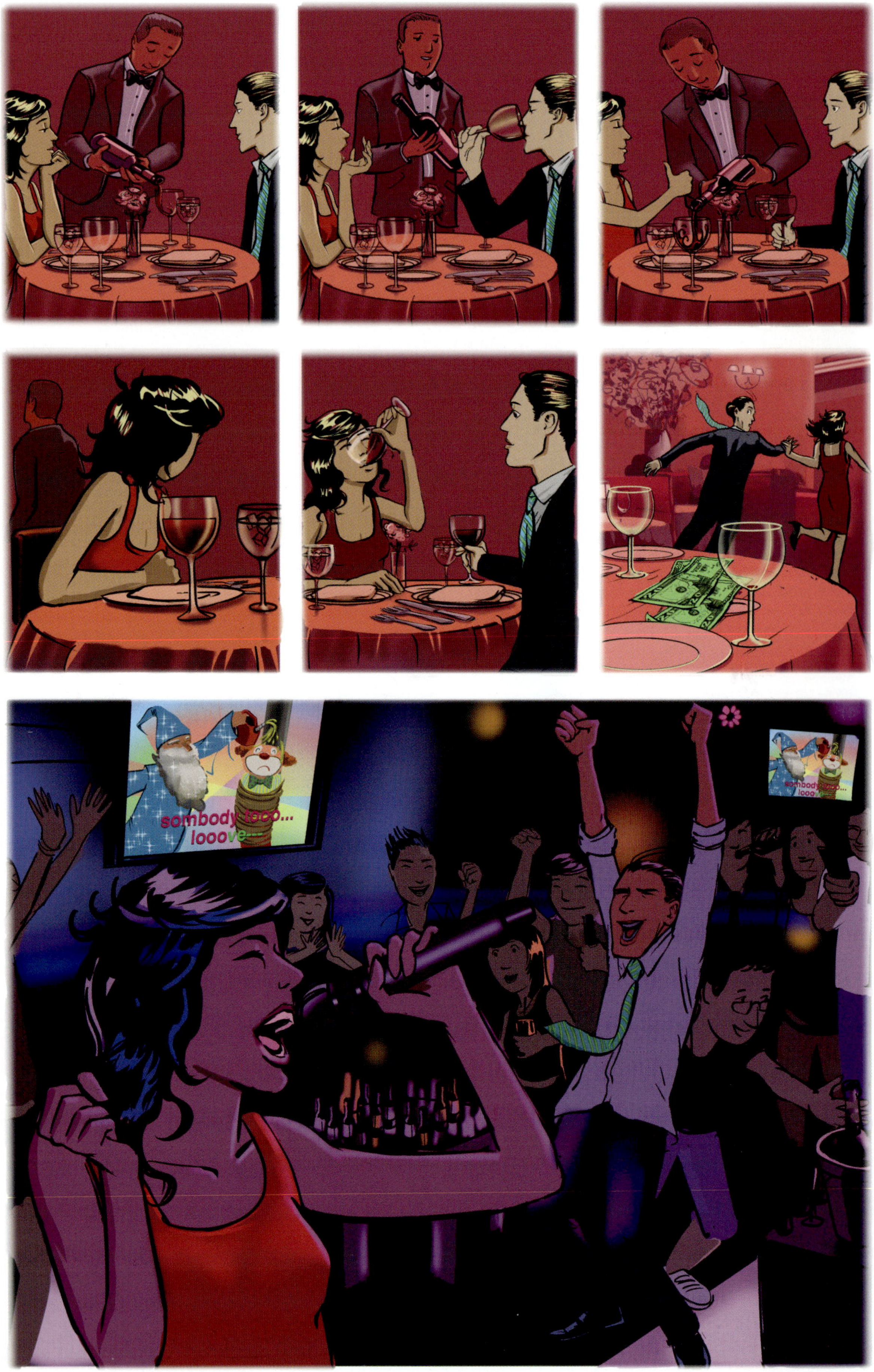

TELL ME SOMETHING YOU'VE NEVER TOLD ANYONE ELSE BEFORE.

HMM

MY BLOOD TYPE IS O NEGATIVE.

THAT DOESN'T COUNT AND YOU KNOW IT! IT HAS TO BE INTERESTING!

I'M A UNIVERSAL DONOR! THAT'S INTERESTING!

IT NEEDS TO BE SOMETHING DEEP AND DARK, LIKE YOUR GREATEST FEAR!

GIVE ME AN EXAMPLE.

ARE YOU MAKING COFFEE? MAKE ME SOME TOO!

HEY, I GUESS YOU HAD TO GET TO WORK EARLY TODAY OR SOMETHING. I DON'T REMEMBER YOU MENTIONING ANYTHING ABOUT THAT LAST NIGHT... BUT MAYBE I FORGOT.

OH, YOU LEFT YOUR WALLET HERE. SO DON'T FREAK OUT IF YOU CAN'T FIND IT. ANYWAYS, CALL ME WHEN YOU GET THIS.

CHAPTER 2

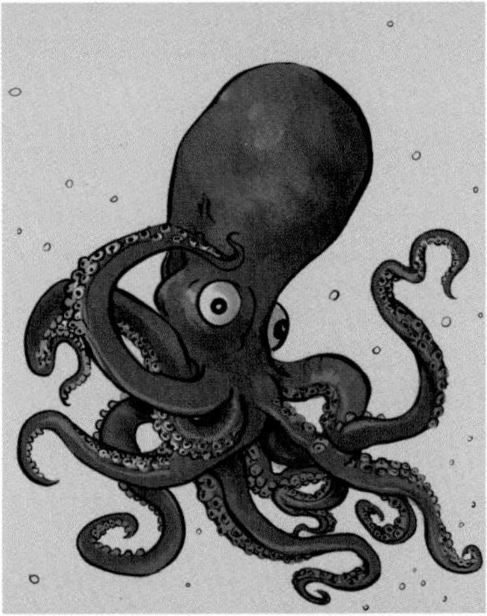

SIX MONTHS AFTER THEIR DISCOVERY, THE ORIGINS OF THE LOST TRIBE REMAIN A MYSTERY.

THEIR CULTURE AND LANGUAGE BEARS NO RESEMBLANCE TO THAT OF ANY OTHER TRIBE WITHIN HUNDREDS OF MILES.

SHHHH,
BE VERY, VERY QUIET,
I'M HUNTING BUNNIES.
HAHAHA.

NOW I GOT YOU --
YOU, BUNNY! HAHAHAH.

ARE YOU TRYIN' TO
GET YOURSELF IN TROUBLE
WITH THE LAW? THIS AINT
BUNNY HUNTING SEASON!

IT'S NOT?!

HEH HEH...

-OTTER SEASON.
   -BUNNY SEASON!!
-OTTER SEASON.
   -BUNNY SEASON!!
-OTTER SEASON.
   -BUNNY THEASON!!!
-BUNNY SEASON.

I SAY IT'S
OTTER SEASON,
AND I SAY: FIRE!!

BOOM!!..

HAHAHAHAH-
HAH--

THAT WAS A CLIP FROM THE JUST RELEASED *"TRIUMPH INTO DARKNESS,"* A BRAVE NEW FILM BY **WERNER NOTZOG** WHO HAS BEEN SO KIND AS TO ALLOW US INSIDE HIS OFFICE.

WELCOME.

SO THIS IS WHERE IT ALL HAPPENS?

THIS IS WHERE I COME TO *RELAX.*

DIRECTING IS NOT FOR THE FAINTHEARTED.

IT IS FOR THOSE WHO HAVE TRAVELLED ON FOOT, WHO HAVE WORKED AS BOUNCERS IN SEX CLUBS OR AS WARDENS IN LUNATIC ASYLUMS.

IN SHORT: FOR THOSE WHO HAVE A SENSE OF POETRY.

WHILE MAKING THIS FILM, YOU INTERVIEWED DOZENS OF TRIBESMEN WITHOUT A TRANSLATOR.

LINGUISTS DO NOT YET UNDERSTAND THEIR LANGUAGE. NO TRANSLATOR EXISTS.

YET SOMEHOW YOU MADE YOURSELF UNDERSTOOD. AND WE, THROUGH THE LANGUAGE OF THE MOVING IMAGE, WERE MADE TO UNDERSTAND THEM.

PERHAPS. THOUGH PERHAPS IT WAS MADNESS.

ARE YOU FAMILIAR WITH MADNESS?

ONCE, IN AN ATTEMPT TO TRULY UNDERSTAND WHAT IT MEANS TO BE LONELY, I SPENT SIX MONTHS INSIDE AN INACTIVE VOLCANO. BY THE NINTH DAY I WAS CONVINCED THAT MY SOCKS WERE GODS.

AND THEY WERE, IN FACT, NOT.

WHAT DO THESE TRIBESMEN HAVE TO TEACH US ABOUT BEING HUMAN?

HUMANNESS IS THE ABILITY TO CREATE SOMETHING OUT OF NOTHING. TO CREATE A SYMPHONY OUT OF WOOD AND METAL, TO CREATE SHARED LAUGHTER FROM INCOMPREHENSIBLE GIBBERISH, TO CREATE GODS FROM THE UNKNOWN.

THE MOST BASIC HUMAN DESIRE IS NOT FOR FOOD OR SEX. IT IS A NEED TO MAKE SENSE OF A CHAOTIC AND NONSENSICAL WORLD.

IT IS INTERESTING THAT YOU MENTION "CREATING SOMETHING FROM NOTHING." YOU HAVE BEEN CRITICIZED FOR TAKING EXTRAORDINARY LICENSE IN DOCUMENTARY FILMMAKING.

I AM NOT INTERESTED IN THE KIND OF CINEMA VERITE THAT POSTULATES THAT YOU SHOULD BE UNOBTRUSIVE LIKE A FLY ON THE WALL. I WILL BE PRESENT. I DON'T WANT TO BE A FLY. I WANT TO BE A HORNET THAT GOES IN AND STINGS.

IF THAT REQUIRES ME TO STAGE A SCENE IN A DOCUMENTARY, SO BE IT.

WE MUST RELEASE OURSELVES FROM REALITY IN ORDER TO COMPREHEND THE TRUTH.

31

BEEEEEEEEEP

WHERE ARE YOU?! LOOK, I'M NOT ONE OF THOSE CLINGY GIRLS WHO NEEDS TO KNOW WHERE HER BOYFRIEND IS AT ALL TIMES. I'M SO FAR FROM THAT.

THAT BEING SAID. I'M ALSO NOT ONE OF THOSE GIRLS WHO PUTS SO MUCH ENERGY INTO BEING COOL AND NOT CLINGY THAT IT'S OBVIOUS THAT I'M SUPPRESSING SOME DADDY-ABANDONMENT ISSUES OR SOMETHI--

--ALEXANDRA.

OH, HEY. I WAS JUST FINISHING A CALL.

ACTUALLY, COULD I TALK TO YOU ABOUT WHAT REALLY HAPPENED IN THIS SCENE?

CLICK

HE'S *DEAD?* HOW? I WAS JUST WITH HIM THIS M--

DO I NEED A LAWYER?

HOW WELL DID YOU KNOW YOUR BOYFRIEND?

BZZZZZZZZ

MCARDLE HERE.

...

BUT I THINK I'VE FOUND SOMETHING HERE THAT'S POTENTIALLY--

...

I DO, SIR.

I UNDERSTAND.

WHAT DO YOU MEAN, *HE'S DEAD?*

WHAT DO YOU MEAN, WHAT DO I MEAN? *HE'S DEAD.*

OH, MY GOD.

ARE YOU OKAY?

YEAH. THANKS.

I MEAN, I *THINK* HE'S DEAD.

YOU'RE BEING VERY CONFUSING RIGHT NOW. SHOULD I BE HUGGING YOU OR NOT?

YES.

WAIT.

I DON'T KNOW.

RIGHT BEFORE HE LEFT THE DETECTIVE GOT A PHONE CALL.

WHEN IT FINISHED HE SUDDENLY SAID THE CASE WAS 'RESOLVED' AND WALKED OUT.

SO MAYBE IT WAS A MISUNDERSTANDING.

THEN *WHERE'S* TODD?

I'M SURE HE JUST FORGOT TO TELL YOU WHAT HE WAS UP TO TODAY.

36

WHY DON'T YOU CALL ONE OF HIS FRIENDS AND SEE IF THEY KNOW WHAT HE'S UP TO?

I DON'T KNOW WHO ANY OF HIS FRIENDS ARE.

REALLY? HE NEVER INTRODUCED YOU TO HIS *FRIENDS?* YOU GUYS HAVE BEEN TOGETHER FOR, LIKE, SIX MONTHS.

IT'S NOT WEIRD. WE'RE AT THE STAGE IN OUR RELATIONSHIP WHERE THAT'S PROBABLY THE NEXT THING THAT WILL HAPPEN.

WHAT?

WHAT ARE YOU TALKING ABOUT?

THAT *LOOK.*

WHAT LOOK?

THAT LOOK THAT SAYS: "I'M NOT A RELATIONSHIP EXPERT OR ANYTHING AND I DON'T WANT TO GET TOO INVOLVED IN YOUR BUSINESS, BUT I THINK IT'S DEFINITELY WEIRD THAT YOU HAVEN'T MET HIS FRIENDS YET AND I KNOW YOU ALSO THINK IT'S WEIRD BUT NEITHER OF US IS GOING TO SAY ANYTHING ABOUT IT RIGHT NOW BECAUSE THE TIMING DOESN'T FEEL RIGHT."

STOP WITH THE LOOK!

I CAN'T! HAVE YOU CHECKED HIS OFFICE? WHERE DOES HE WORK?

UMM... SOME PLACE THAT DOES SOMETHING FOR THE INTERNET. I THINK IT'S CLOSE TO A MCDONALDS.

WILL YOU JUST HELP ME FIGURE OUT WHAT'S GOING ON HERE?

FINE. LET'S START BY CHECKING OUT HIS APARTMENT.

YOU *DO* KNOW WHERE HIS APARTMENT IS, RIGHT?

WE ALWAYS STAYED OVER AT OUR PLACE BECAUSE HE SAID IT WAS NICER.

HOW IS THAT *POSSIBLE?* WE HAVE A *RAT* THAT LIVES IN OUR *MAILBOX!*

OH MY GOD. WHO WAS I *DATING?*

CRAP. I HAVE TO GO ON A STAKEOUT.

PLEASE DON'T LEAVE ME ALONE RIGHT NOW.

DON'T FREAK OUT. I WATCH LOT OF MY-BOYFRIEND-WAS-A-SECRET-PSYCHO TV SHOWS. ALL OF THEM END WITH THE GIRL STRONGER THAN WHEN SHE STARTED.

WHAT WOULD MAKE A DETECTIVE SUDDENLY DROP EVERYTHING AND *LEAVE* LIKE THAT?

WELL, IN *MY* EXPERIENCE AS AN OFFICER OF THE CITY--

YOU'RE NOT A COP, FINNEGAN.

AM I NOT PAID BY THE CITY TO UPHOLD JUSTICE? DO I NOT SERVE AND PROTECT?

THAT DOESN'T MAKE YOU A COP.

I DIDN'T USE THE WORD *"COP"*. YOU DID.

ONE THING I'VE OBSERVED IN MY YEARS ON THE FORCE--

DON'T ROLL YOUR EYES! ANY GROUP OF PEOPLE ORGANIZED FOR A SPECIFIC ACTIVITY CAN BE CALLED A "FORCE".

THIS MISTAKE PROBABLY HAPPENED BECAUSE OF POLITICAL PRESSURE TO FOCUS ON "GLAMOR POLICING ISSUES" LIKE KEEPING WALL STREET GRAFFITI FREE. THINGS WILL BE DIFFERENT WHEN I RUN THINGS.

NYPD. IS THIS AN EMERGENCY?

UM, NO. I WAS JUST WONDERING--

YOU KNOW, IT'S NOT A BIG DEAL. I CAN CALL BACK IF YOU GUYS ARE BUSY RIGHT NOW. SOMETIME WHEN THERE ARE NO CRIMES BEING COMMITTED.

MA'AM ARE YOU BEING HELD HOSTAGE AND DID YOUR KIDNAPPER WALK INTO THE ROOM AFTER YOU STARTED MAKING THIS PHONE CALL THEN SILENTLY SIGNAL TO YOU TO END THIS INTERACTION IN AN UNSUSPICIOUS FASHION? IF SO, JUST SAY "THANK YOU" AND HANG UP AND WE WILL SEND A TEAM TO YOUR LOCATION IMMEDIATELY.

NO, NO. DON'T DO THAT. I'M **NOT** BEING HELD HOSTAGE!

DAMMIT, I NEVER GET ANY HOSTAGES.

WHAT IS YOUR CALL REGARDING?

A HOMICIDE DETECTIVE CAME BY MY OFFICE TODAY ASKING ABOUT *TODD LEE.* I WAS WONDERING IF THERE'S BEEN ANY PROGRESS IN HIS CASE.

LET ME CHECK.

♪ ♫ ♪♫ ♪♫

IT SAYS HERE THAT THE TODD LEE CASE IS CLOSED.

YOU FOUND HIM?!

I'M NOT SURE. THE FILE IS SEALED.

I'M NOT SURE HOW I FEEL ABOUT THIS.

SOUNDS LIKE YOU FEEL "UNSURE."

THANK GOD.

WHAT?

HE'S REALLY NOT HERE. MY WORST CASE SCENARIO WAS THAT THIS WAS ALL A RUSE TO BREAK UP WITH ME.

OBVIOUSLY, THE SECOND WORST CASE SCENARIO IS THAT SOMEONE STRANGLED HIM.

THIS APARTMENT IS WAY NICER THAN OURS.

YOU DON'T HAVE TO STAND IN THE TUB TO BRUSH YOUR TEETH.

YEAH. WHY WOULD HE *LIE* TO ME ABOUT HIS PLACE?

WELL, WHAT ARE WE LOOKING FOR HERE?

I DON'T KNOW. WHAT DO CLUES USUALLY LOOK LIKE?

WHAT ABOUT THIS?

THOUGH I SUPPOSE IT COULD JUST BE A PHOTO OF HIM AND HIS DAD.

IT'S REALLY HARD TO TELL THE DIFFERENCE BETWEEN CLUES AND NOTHING. BUT JUST IN CASE...

DON'T YOU HAVE A FRIEND BACK AT THE OFFICE WHO CAN RUN PLATES FOR YOU?

YES.

CAN YOU ASK HIM TO LOOK UP UUL724?

OH, I WAS TALKING ABOUT ACTUAL PLATES. THE KIND YOU EAT OFF. RICK CAN CHECK TO SEE IF THEY'RE WITHIN REGULATIONS.

WHAT ARE YOU DOING?

CHECKING WHAT'S ON HIS DVR.

HOW WILL THAT HELP US?

IT WON'T. BUT AREN'T YOU CURIOUS ABOUT WHO THIS GUY REALLY IS?

Repeat, HD, "Th (2002), Halfway crab gauntlet...

SEE? A LOT OF NATIONAL GEOGRAPHIC AND DISCOVERY CHANNEL.

HE'S AN INTELLECTUAL.

I DON'T KNOW THAT MANY INTELLECTUALS WHO WATCH THREE DIFFERENT APARTMENT MAKEOVER SHOWS.

RACHEL MADDOW.

"GIGLI: SNYDER CUT"

"THE DAILY SHOW"

A SEASON PASS FOR ALL FOUR HOURS OF THE 'TODAY SHOW' SET TO "SAVE UNTIL I DELETE"!

YOU'RE SEEING WHAT YOU WANT TO SEE!

SO ARE YOU!

Ring Ring!!

Ring Ring!!

SHOULD WE ANSWER?

ABSOLUTELY NOT. IT'S ILLEGAL FOR US TO BE HERE. ALSO IT'S JUST A PHONE. THERE'S NO NEED TO WHISPER.

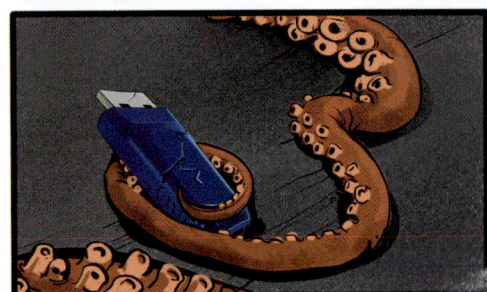

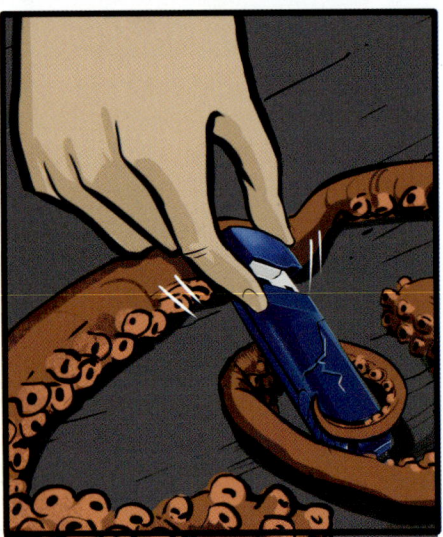

WHAT THE *FUCK?*

sigh

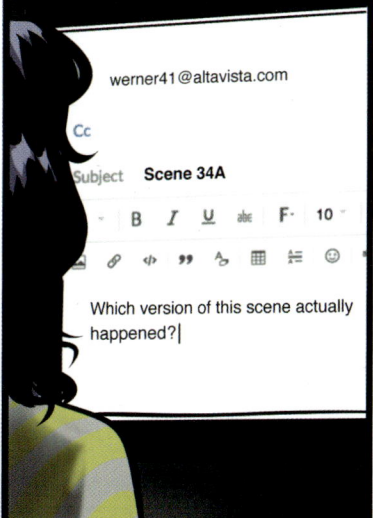

werner41@altavista.com

Cc

Subject   **Scene 34A**

B *I* U̲ abc F· 10

Which version of this scene actually happened?|

CLICK

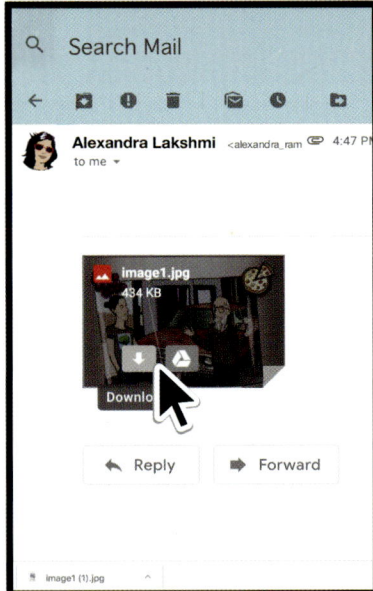

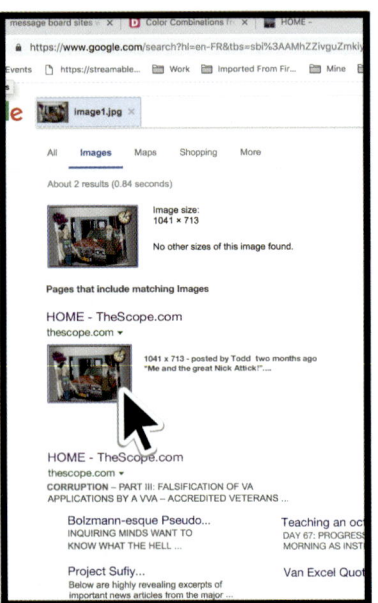
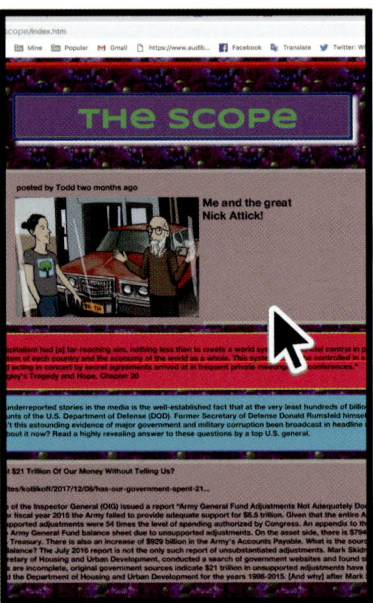

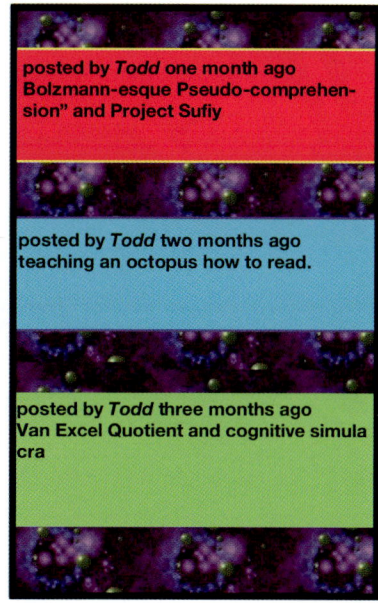

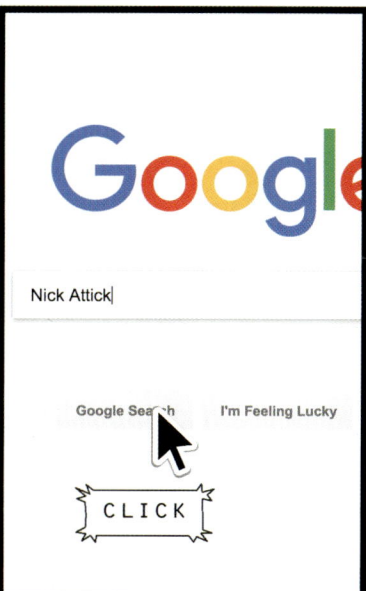

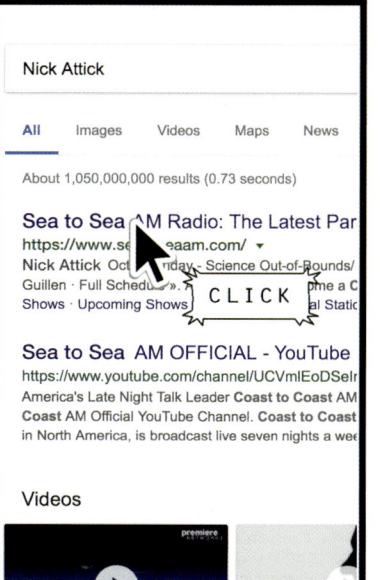

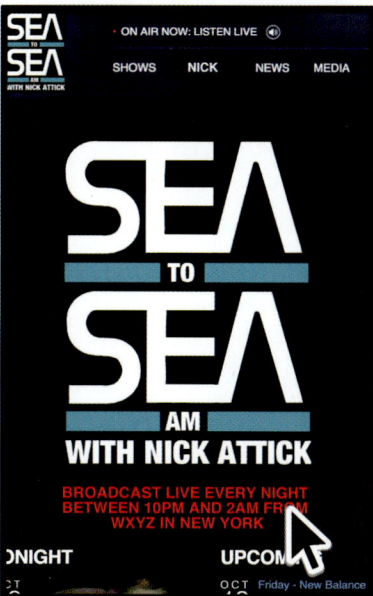

--THE GOVERNMENT, THAT'S WHO.

THAT'S OBVIOUS. BUT WHY?

I WISH I KNEW, NICK.

I JUST FIND IT UNBELIEVABLE HOW, IN OVER A DECADE, NOT **ONE** PERSON IN THE SCIENTIFIC COMMUNITY HAS BEEN ABLE TO EXPLAIN THE SOUND.

IT'S VERY SUSPICIOUS. I MEAN, IT TOOK LESS TIME, FROM PROPOSAL TO EXECUTION, TO GO TO THE MOON.

HAHAHAHAH- HAHA!!!!!

FOR THOSE OF YOU JUST JOINING US, I'M HERE WITH DR. ELVIS TROY AND WE'RE DISCUSSING--

BLOOP

--THAT'S RIGHT, THE BLOOP.

ELVIS, CAN YOU GIVE US A QUICK PRIMER ON THIS NOISE, IN CASE WE HAVE ANY SEA TO SEA LISTENERS WHO'VE BEEN LIVING IN A CONE OF IGNORANCE FOR THE PAST FIFTEEN YEARS.

IT ALL STARTED BACK IN THE 1960S, DURING THE COLD WAR.

THE GOLDEN AGE OF SECRET PLOTS.

IN AN ATTEMPT TO TRACK SOVIET SUBMARINES, THE NAVY BUILT THIS GLOBAL SYSTEM OF UNDERWATER MICROPHONES, OR HYDROPHONES, CALLED THE SOUND SURVEILLANCE SYSTEM, OR **SOSUS**, TO MONITOR LOW FREQUENCY SOUNDS IN THE SOFAR CHANNEL.

MORE FAMILIARLY KNOWN AS THE DEEP SOUND CHANNEL.

OF COURSE, OF COURSE. NOW THE SOFAR IS A LAYER OF THE OCEAN WHERE LOW FREQUENCY SOUNDS BOUNCE AROUND, UNABLE TO LEAVE THE CHANNEL, TRAVELING FOR THOUSANDS OF MILES BEFORE DISSIPATING.

SO THE MILITARY PRESUMABLY BUILT THIS THING TO MONITOR THE SOVIETS.

THAT'S RIGHT.

WAS IT SUCCESSFUL? DID THIS SOUND SURVEILLANCE SYSTEM PREVENT ANY ENEMY ACTIVITIES?

I DON'T THINK IT'S A COINCIDENCE THAT THERE'S NEVER BEEN A SINGLE SUCCESSFUL SOVIET SUBMARINE ATTACK ON AMERICAN SOIL.

MY FAVORITE PART OF THIS STORY IS HOW THE POLITICIANS COULDN'T TAKE CREDIT FOR SOSUS'S SUCCESS BECAUSE THEY DIDN'T EVEN ADMIT IT EXISTED UNTIL 1991!

IF THEY KEPT THAT FROM US, WHAT ELSE MIGHT THEY BE KEEPING FROM US?

SURE WE'RE PARANOID.

BUT ARE WE PARANOID *ENOUGH?!*

HAHAHAHAH-HAHA!!!!

SO WHAT HAPPENED TO THESE HYDROPHONES AFTER THE COLD WAR ENDED?

CIVILIAN SCIENTISTS -- YOUR OCEANOGRAPHERS, YOUR MARINE BIOLOGISTS, BASICALLY ANYONE WITH A PAIR OF GLASSES AND SOME INTEREST WERE GIVEN ACCESS TO THE SYSTEM.

AND WHAT DID THEY HEAR?

AT FIRST, IT WAS WHAT YOU'D EXPECT. WHALE SOUNDS, UNDERWATER EARTHQUAKES, ICE SHEET COLLAPSES...

THEN, IN 1997, WE HEARD--

BLOOP

--THE BLOOP.

LISTENERS CAN FIND THE AUDIO ON THE U.S. NATIONAL OCEANIC AND ATMOSPHERIC ADMINISTRATION--

--CONVERSATIONALLY KNOWN AS *NOAA*--

--WEBSITE*. THIS THING WAS SO BIG THAT THE GOVERNMENT COULDN'T PRETEND IT DIDN'T HAPPEN.

TELL US MORE ABOUT THE NATURE OF THIS SOUND.

WELL, THE BLOOP VARIES RAPIDLY IN FREQUENCY, MUCH LIKE KNOWN SOUNDS MADE BY UNDERWATER BEASTS. SO IT'S ANIMAL IN NATURE.

THE INTERESTING PART IS IT'S *AMPLITUDE*.: THE BLOOP WAS DETECTED BY SENSORS 4,800KM APART. MEANING IT IS MUCH, *MUCH* LOUDER THAN ANY OTHER ANIMAL NOISE EVER HEARD. THERE'S SOME GIANT CREATURE DOWN THERE. SOME MARINE MONSTER MULTIPLE TIMES LARGER THAN ANY KNOWN LIFEFORM ON EARTH.

SOSUS HAS EXISTED FOR OVER 60 YEARS, RIGHT?

AND IT'S NEVER DETECTED ANYTHING LIKE THIS.

SO WHY HAS THIS BEAST, AFTER DECADES OF SILENCE, SUDDENLY DECIDED TO START SPEAKING?

ALWAYS A PLEASURE TO HAVE YOU ON THE SHOW, ELVIS.

PLEASURE TO BE HERE, NICK.

LISTENERS, WE'LL BE RIGHT BACK AFTER THIS COMMERCIAL BREAK

* WWW.PMEL.NOAA.GOV/VENTS/ACOUSTICS/SOUNDS/BLOOP.WAV

UM, HELLO.

I'M ALEXANDRA. I THINK WE HAVE A FRIEND IN COMMON AND **MONDO** HERE WAS SO KIND AS TO...

...NOT DO ANYTHING WHEN I ASKED IF I COULD JUST HANG OUT AND MEET YOU.

HOW CAN I HELP YOU?

I WANT TO KNOW WHAT HAPPENED TO TODD LEE?

IS THIS A WHAT'S THE FREQUENCY KENNETH SITUATION? I'VE ALWAYS WANTED ONE OF THOSE.

I KNEW TODD. IT LOOKS LIKE YOU DID TOO. HE DISAPPEARED YESTERDAY AND I WAS WONDERING IF YOU HAD ANY IDEAS AS TO WHY?

ARE YOU A COP?

NO.

BUT I MIGHT HAVE BEEN IN A PAST LIFE?

I DON'T REMEMBER TAKING THIS. BUT IT LOOKS LIKE IT'S FROM LAST YEAR'S CONSPIRACY COMMUNITY CONVENTION.

I *CAN'T* BELIEVE HE WAS INVOLVED IN ALL THIS STUFF. HE SEEMED SO *NORMAL*.

OF COURSE HE DID. FOR UNCLEAR REASONS THERE AREN'T A LOT OF WOMEN IN THE CONSPIRACY COMMUNITY. WE BELIEVE IT'S A RESULT OF A CONSPIRACY TO PREVENT OUR PROCREATION.

AS A RESULT COMMUNITY MEMBERS DOWNPLAY THE DEPTH OF THEIR SUSPICIONS AROUND GENETIC FEMALES.

RANDOM QUESTION: ARE YOU FERTILE?

shrug

I HAVE TO BE BACK ON AIR IN 15 SECONDS.

WXYZ
710AM

SEA TO SEA
AM
WITH NICK ATTICK

I THOUGHT YOU WANTED TO HELP PEOPLE DISCOVER THE *TRUTH*.

THERE'S A BAR IN QUEENS CALLED **GIVE ME DEATH.** MEET ME THERE AFTER THE SHOW.

YOU'RE LISTENING TO **SEA TO SEA** WITH NICK ATTICK. SHINING A LIGHT ON THE SECRETS OF THE UNIVERSE SINCE 1991.

WELCOME BACK TO SEA TO SEA-ERS. I'M JOINED NOW IN THE STUDIO BY **STARLIGHT,** WHO BELIEVES SHE IS A REINCARNATION OF THE VIRGIN MARY.

CAN I SMOKE IN HERE?

WHATEVER YOU HAVE ON TAP.

WE DON'T ACCEPT ANY CURRENCY CREATED BY GOVERNMENT FIAT.

UM, OKAY.

SO, HOW DO I PAY?

ANY NON-RENEWABLE COMMODITY WILL WORK.

IT'S FAIRLY INEFFICIENT TO SHAVE ONE BEER'S WORTH OF GOLD OFF A CHAIN. MOST PEOPLE PAY IN GASOLINE FOR CONVENIENCE REASONS.

I'LL GET THIS ROUND, DEVIN.

YOU GUYS ARE TODD'S **BEST** FRIENDS?

SQUAWK!

I'LL BE HONEST, I FEEL A LITTLE WEIRD THAT TODD NEVER INTRODUCED ME TO HIS FRIENDS. I THOUGHT WE WERE CLOSE BUT NOW I'M DISCOVERING HE HAD THIS WHOLE LIFE DIDN'T KNOW ABOUT.

I'M SURE YOU GUYS ALSO FEEL WEIRD. BECAUSE HE NEVER INTRODUCED YOU TO ME.

NOT AT ALL. OUR FRIENDSHIP, HAS AN INTIMACY THAT TRANSCENDS THE SEXUAL REALM.

DO YOU KNOW WHAT THE LARGEST EROGENOUS ZONE IS?

THE MIND.

THE HUMAN PENIS.

WHAT WAS TODD INVESTIGATING THAT WAS SO DANGEROUS?

ALL THE USUAL STUFF: TALKING TO ANIMALS, DEVELOPING PEDAGOGIC TOOLS TO TEACH ANIMALS TO READ--

--MAPPING WHERE DIFFERENT SPECIES FALL ON THE POLITICAL SPECTRUM.

CATS ARE *LIBERTARIAN.*

IF POKING AROUND THIS STUFF IS PISSING OFF POWERFUL PEOPLE, HOW COME NOBODY'S COME AFTER US?

Mirltu Treeordrore!

Milton Theodore!

MILTON THEODORE?

M. THEODORE! HE CALLED TODD'S APARTMENT LAST NIGHT!

THEODORE IS INVOLVED IN THIS?

NICE MEMORY, XAVIER.

Mom! Can you bring me some toilet paper?

THAT'S. ENOUGH.

SQUAWK!

TODD REACHED OUT TO THEODORE FOR SOME ADVICE LAST WEEK. I'M NOT SURE WHAT ABOUT, BUT HE DIDN'T MAKE IT SEEM LIKE A BIG DEAL.

WE DIDN'T KEEP IMPORTANT THINGS SECRET FROM EACH OTHER.

WELL, JUST IN CASE YOU HAVE NO IDEA WHAT YOU'RE TALKING ABOUT, I'LL CHECK IN WITH HIM.

IT'S NOT THAT EASY, SWEETHEART. THEODORE IS A VERY, VERY PRIVATE MAN. IT TAKES MONTHS, IF NOT YEARS, OF BUILDING TRUST WITHIN THE CONSPIRACY COMMUNITY TO EVEN GET AN INTRO--

FOUND IT.

YOU SHOULD GO HOME. I CAN TAKE CARE OF MYSELF.

hisss

WELL, *SHE* WAS WEIRD.

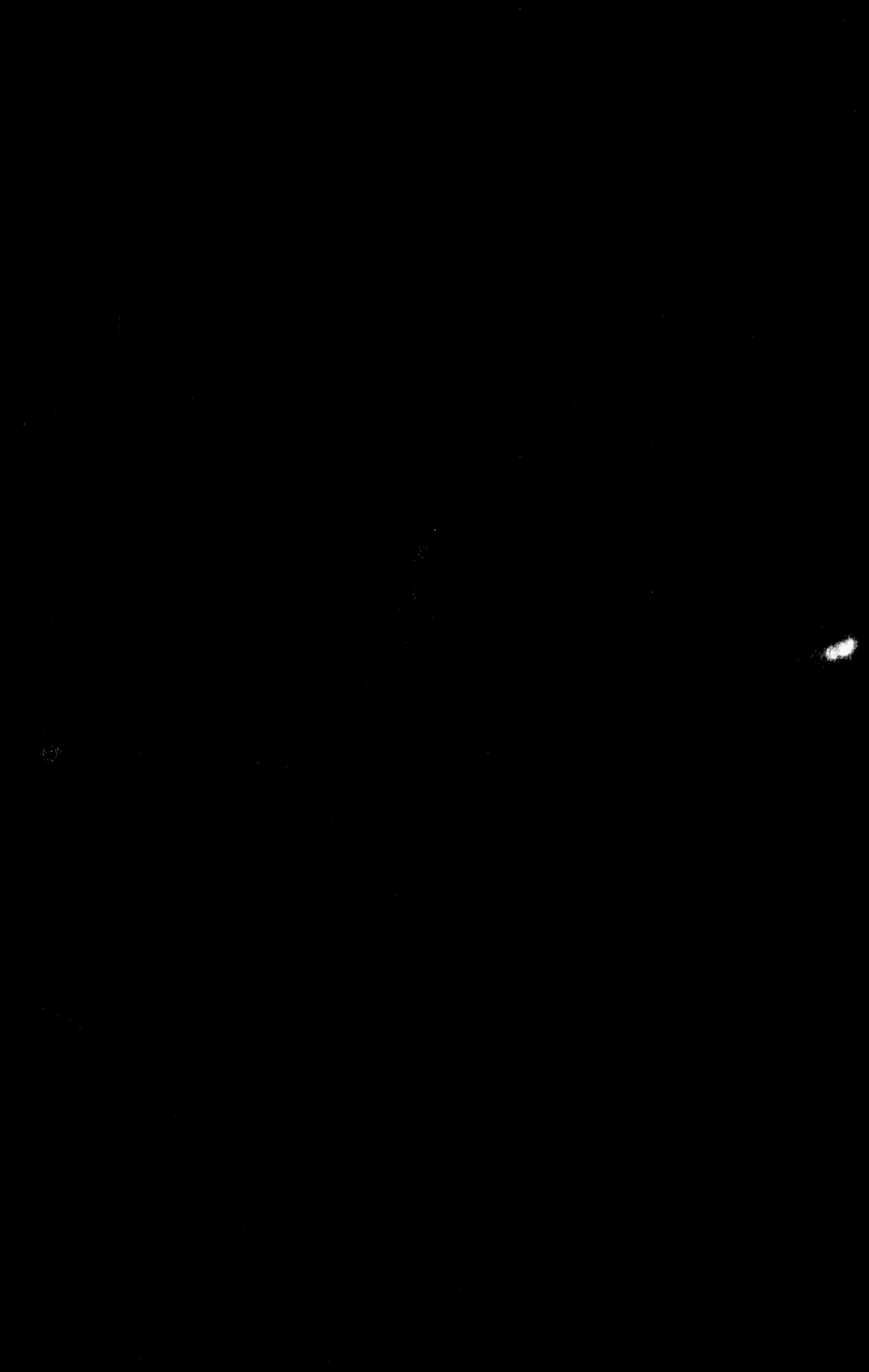

CHAPTER 4

WHAT'S HAPPENING?

JUST KEEP ACTING NORMAL.

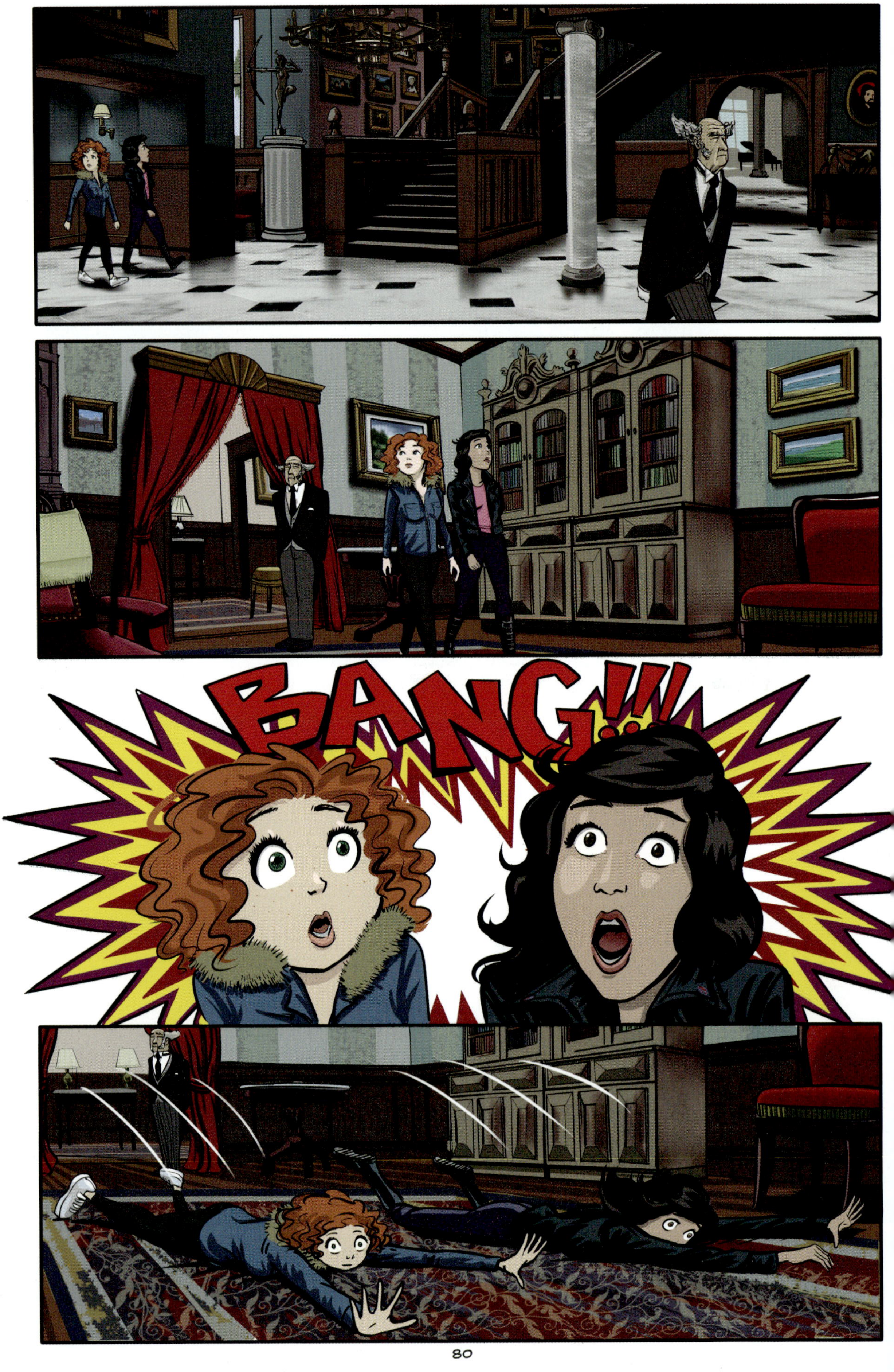

BANG!!!

SIR, YOUR GUESTS.

WOULD YOU CARE FOR ANY REFRESHMENTS? WATER, TEA, COCAINE?

UM, NO.

I'D LOVE AN ARNOLD PALMER.

IS IT GIRL SCOUT COOKIE TIME AGAIN ALREADY?

HOW DID YOU KNOW TODD LEE?

I SUPPOSE YOU WANT TO KNOW ABOUT THE BUNNY.

I DIDN'T ACTUALLY KNOW TODD PERSONALLY.

HE CONTACTED ME A FEW DAYS AGO REGARDING SOME WORK MY GREAT GRANDFATHER DID WHEN HE WAS IN THE MILITARY.

HE WAS THE LAST *HAPPY* THEODORE.

WHY WAS TODD INTERESTED IN HIM?

FOLLOW ME.

IN ORDER TO SUPPORT HIS FAMILY, MY GREAT GRANDFATHER ENLISTED IN THE UNITED STATES ARMY.

OBVIOUSLY, HE DIDN'T NEED TO WORK TO SUPPORT HIS FAMILY.

OH, HE DID. WE THEODORES DIDN'T HAVE ANY OF THIS, UNTIL THE FINAL ACT OF ELLIOT'S LIFE.

BECAUSE OF HIS MYRIAD MEDICAL ISSUES--SCOLIOSIS, OVERACTIVE GALL BLADDER, LIMITED COLOR PERCEPTION, JUST TO NAME A FEW--ELIOT NEVER SAW ACTIVE DUTY.

INSTEAD HE WAS ASSIGNED TO BE A LOW LEVEL CLERK ON AN ANIMAL HUSBANDRY PROJECT.

WHY WAS THE MILITARY RAISING ANIMALS?

GREAT QUESTION.

THE GOAL OF THE PROJECT WAS TO DEVELOP MORE PRODUCTIVE STRAINS OF ANIMALS IN ORDER TO AVOID SHORTAGES DURING WAR TIMES.

THE THINKING AT THE TIME BEING, WARS GET UNPOPULAR, ONE, BECAUSE OF THE YOUNG MEN DYING OVERSEAS AND, TWO, BECAUSE OF THE HARDSHIPS FACED BY THOSE BACK HOME.

THE MILITARY IS ALWAYS DEVELOPING NEW AND INNOVATIVE WAYS TO PROTECT OUR SOLDIERS. WHY NOT, *SOME SNIVELING PENCIL PUSHER* WONDERED, ALSO DEVELOP WAYS TO LIMIT THE HARDSHIPS FACED AT HOME?

DAMMIT! MISSED.

THE SCIENTISTS THAT ELIOT WORKED FOR QUICKLY DISCOVERED THAT IN ADDITION TO SIZE AND MILK PRODUCTION, THEY COULD ALSO BREED SPECIMENS FOR INTELLIGENCE. WONDERING HOW FAR THEY COULD PUSH THIS TRAIT, THEY DECIDED TO EXPERIMENT ON A SPECIES THAT, AS THE POPULAR SAYING GOES, FUCKED LIKE CRAZY.

RABBITS?

THE EXPERIMENTS WERE AN INCREDIBLE SUCCESS. WITHIN TWENTY GENERATIONS RABBITS THAT COULD SOLVE MAZES TO GET SUGAR PELLET REWARDS WERE BRED.

WITHIN TWO HUNDRED GENERATIONS THEY HAD RABBITS WHO COULD SOLVE MAZES NOT FOR ANY FOOD REWARD, BUT JUST FOR THE INTELLECTUAL SATISFACTION OF SOLVING A PROBLEM

BY THE SIX-HUNDREDTH GENERATION THEY HAD SPECIMENS CAPABLE OF PUSHING AROUND WOOD BLOCKS TO CREATE THEIR OWN MAZES.

AND IN THE NINE HUNDRED AND SIXTY-FOURTH GENERATION, A MERE FIVE YEARS AND NINE MONTHS INTO THE PROGRAM, *HE* WAS BORN. THREE STANDARD DEVIATIONS TO THE RIGHT OF THE INTELLIGENCE MEAN.

THAT FUCKER WAS A *GENIUS*.

IF HE MURDERS US, I'M GOING TO BE SO PISSED THAT I WORKED OUT INSTEAD OF JUST EATING PIZZA LAST NIGHT.

HIS OFFICIAL NAME WAS R249X532. AND MY GREAT GRANDFATHER WAS TRANSFIXED BY HIM. THAT NIGHT, HE WROTE IN HIS JOURNAL, "THE ALMIGHTY HAS DELIVERED TO ME A MUSE."

AFTER DECADES SPENT PAINFULLY AWARE OF HIS LACK OF CREATIVITY, ELIOT THEODORE'S FORTUNES CHANGED. NEVER IN THE HISTORY OF ART HAS INSPIRATION STRUCK MORE SUDDENLY AND OVERWHELMINGLY.

‹CLICK›

SO, I HAVE A QUESTION.

THE SKELETON IS A FABRICATION, BUILT ON THE RECOMMENDATION OF MY THERAPIST. HE THOUGHT *SPITTING* AND *URINATING* ON IT MAY HELP WITH MY ANGER ISSUES. IT DID NOT. ANY OTHER *QUESTIONS?*

ONLY MILLIONS.

AS I'M SURE YOU'VE SURMISED, ELIOT STARTED MAKING SHORT FILMS ABOUT R249X532.

PROJECT SUFIY WAS CLASSIFIED--

BUT SINCE HE WAS MAKING SILLY CARTOONS, HE FIGURED THE MILITARY WOULDN'T CARE. HE WAS RIGHT AT FIRST. BUT THEN HE MADE ONE THAT GAVE TOO MUCH OF THE TRUTH AWAY.

VVVVIP

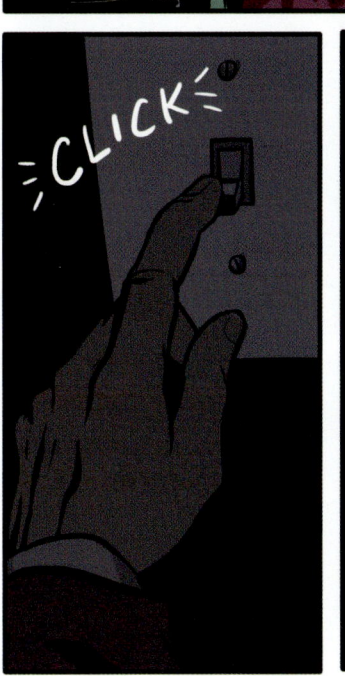

CLICK

WRRRRRRR

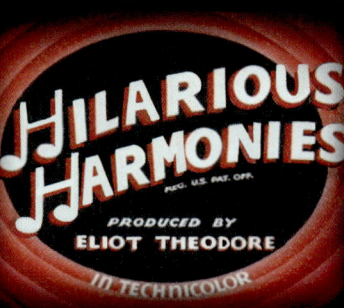

The End!

WHAT WAS THAT?

THAT INSOLENT FUCK RUINED MY LIFE.

SO, WE SHOULD GET GOING.

YOU THINK I'M CRAZY, DON'T YOU?! GO AHEAD AND LAUGH. BUT KNOW THAT YOUR LAUGHTER IS PAID FOR WITH IGNORANCE! AN IGNORANCE THAT YOU CAN NO LONGER AFFORD NOW THAT YOU HAVE SEEN THE EVIDENCE.

ARE YOU CLAIMING THAT EVERYTHING IN THAT CARTOON WAS REAL?

NOT EVERYTHING. SOME OF THE CHARACTERS WERE COMPOSITES OF TWO OR MORE REAL PEOPLE. AND DIALOG WAS CREATED TO MAKE THE INTERNAL MINDSET OF THE RABBIT MORE CLEAR.

I'M NOT INSANE.

BUT ALL OF THE MAJOR EVENTS TOOK PLACE. THAT PART WHERE THE SOLDIER WAS SHOT OUT OF A TANK. THAT WAS BASED ON A REAL INCIDENT THAT MY GREAT GRANDFATHER WITNESSED.

IF IT WASN'T FOR HIS QUICK ACTION, AN ARMY STAFF SERGEANT WOULD HAVE BEEN VAPORIZED !

BUT WAS THE BRASS THANKFUL FOR HIS ACTIONS? WAS HE REWARDED FOR SAVING A FELLOW SOLDIER?

BASED ON YOUR TONE OF VOICE, I'M GOING TO GUESS NO. PERHAPS EVEN THE OPPOSITE OF REWARDED.

THIS CARTOON NEVER AIRED. WHEN HIS SUPERIORS IN THE MILITARY SAW IT, IT WAS IMMEDIATELY CONFISCATED FOR NATIONAL SECURITY REASONS, AND ELIOT THEODORE WAS *DISHONORABLY DISCHARGED* FROM THE MILITARY, WITHOUT EXPLANATION.

WHY ARE YOU SO UPSET? NO MATTER WHAT YOU THINK HAPPENED BACK THEN, YOU HAVE A GREAT LIFE NOW. YOUR GREAT GRANDFATHER OBVIOUSLY DID ALRIGHT FOR HIMSELF IN THE END.

AT WHAT *COST?* WHEN HE WAS DISCHARGED, ELIOT'S FAMILY BEGGED HIM TO ABANDON HIS CARTOONS AND MOVE ON WITH HIS LIFE. BUT IT WAS TOO LATE. HE WAS OBSESSED. HE SPENT ALL DAY AND NIGHT IN THE GARAGE DRAWING. BARELY EATING, SLEEPING ONLY WHEN HE COLLAPSED FROM EXHAUSTION.

NOT KNOWING WHAT ELSE TO DO, MY GREAT GRANDMOTHER SENT HIM OUT TO LOS ANGELES, IN HOPES THAT HE COULD MAKE A LIVING SELLING HIS CARTOONS, THE POISONED FRUITS OF HIS BROKEN MIND. YOU KNOW HOW THAT WORKED OUT. THE IMBECILES BOUGHT IT, NEVER KNOWING THE DARKNESS THAT THEY WERE LAUGHING AT.

ELIOT WORKED AND WORKED ON HIS CARTOONS. EACH ONE WAS A GOOD-FAITH ATTEMPT TO DESTROY THE RABBIT THAT DESTROYED HIM.

HE PUT THE BUNNY INTO THE MOST DIFFICULT SITUATIONS HE COULD IMAGINE:

IS HE...? OH, GOD. PSSSSSS

IN A PLANE THAT HAD JUST RUN OUT OF GAS,

AT THE BOTTOM OF THE MOUNTAIN DURING A YODELING-INDUCED AVALANCHE,

TRICKED INTO BOARDING A SPACESHIP!

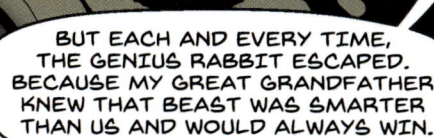

BUT EACH AND EVERY TIME, THE GENIUS RABBIT ESCAPED. BECAUSE MY GREAT GRANDFATHER KNEW THAT BEAST WAS SMARTER THAN US AND WOULD ALWAYS WIN.

I'M CALLING A *TAXI.*

FINALLY, AFTER FOUR HUNDRED WILDLY POPULAR CARTOONS, FOUR HUNDRED ATTEMPTS AT ASSERTING HUMAN SUPREMACY OVER THE ANIMALS, AND AMASSING A FORTUNE SO LARGE THAT NO MEMBER OF HIS FAMILY WOULD EVER HAVE TO WORK AGAIN, ELIOT THEODORE ADMITTED *DEFEAT.*

SO, ONE EVENING HE CAME HOME FROM WORK AND SMOKED A CIGAR WITH A STICK OF DYNAMITE CRAMMED INTO IT AND *KILLED* HIMSELF.

THAT'S THE STORY *TODD LEE* HAD CALLED TO ASK ME ABOUT.

97

SO...

YEAH...

THAT GUY WAS... QUIRKY.

THAT WAS ALL INSANE NONSENSE. RIGHT?

I MEAN, EVERYTHING HE SAID MADE LOGICAL SENSE. WE JUST NEED TO ACCEPT A FEW SMALL ASSUMPTIONS.

ASSUMPTION ONE: WE ARE NOT ON EARTH ANYMORE.

UHP. MY SHOE'S UNTIED.

CRASH!

HOLY CRAP!

CHAPTER 5

IN NATURE, SOME SEE BEAUTY, EVIDENCE OF THE DIVINE

103

I THINK I MAY BE GOING INSANE.

TRAUMATIC INCIDENTS, LIKE THE ONE YOU RECENTLY EXPERIENCED CAN CAUSE ONE TO QUESTION THE VERY MATHEMATICS OF EXISTENCE.

I HAVE NO IDEA WHAT'S HAPPENING ANYMORE.

THAT IS OKAY. THERE IS MUCH THAT WE NOT ONLY DO NOT KNOW BUT CANNOT KNOW AND MUST NEVER KNOW.

THEN WHY BOTHER TRYING TO FIGURE ANYTHING OUT?

THAT IS THE CURSE OF BEING HUMAN. WE NEED A LOGIC TO ORDER THE WORLD AROUND US. SOME FIND IT IN RELIGION, OTHERS IN PHILOSOPHY OR SCIENCE. AT THE CORE OF EACH OF THESE PRACTICES IS NARRATIVE. WE KNOW THESE NARRATIVES CAN BE UNRELIABLE, BUT THAT DOES NOT DIMINISH THEM.

NARRATIVES DON'T **NEED** TO BE UNRELIABLE. FOR ANY EVENT THERE IS ONE TRUE EXPLANATION OUT THERE. IT MIGHT BE HARD TO SUSS OUT. BUT IT EXISTS. ISN'T OUR JOB TO TRY AND FIND IT?

CAN YOU TRUST YOURSELF TO INTERPRET THE FACTS?

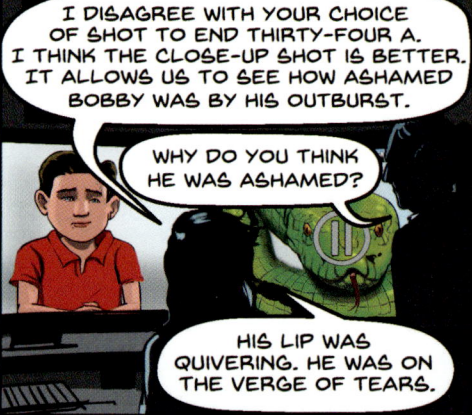

I DISAGREE WITH YOUR CHOICE OF SHOT TO END THIRTY-FOUR A. I THINK THE CLOSE-UP SHOT IS BETTER. IT ALLOWS US TO SEE HOW ASHAMED BOBBY WAS BY HIS OUTBURST.

WHY DO YOU THINK HE WAS ASHAMED?

HIS LIP WAS QUIVERING. HE WAS ON THE VERGE OF TEARS.

WHEN I SHOWED BOBBY THAT FOOTAGE AND ASKED WHAT HE WAS THINKING IN THAT MOMENT, HE TOLD ME HE DIDN'T KNOW. SO I GATHERED UP ALL THE CHILDREN AND STAGED THE SHOT I WANTED TO END THE SCENE WITH.

WAIT. THAT MOMENT DIDN'T REALLY HAPPEN?

THAT DOESN'T MAKE IT ANY LESS TRUE.

HELLO?

WHAT'S THAT *NOISE?*

SORRY. THERE'S A LOT OF EXCITEMENT OVER HERE BECAUSE HOMELAND SECURITY JUST SENT US SOME NEW EXPIRED FOOD TESTING AND REMOVAL ROBOTS.

FRESH

EXPIRED

FRESH

EXPIRED

IT WORKS!!!

YEAAHHH!

WHOO HOO!!!

FOOSH

OH MY GOD!

OUR CYBERWARFARE EXPERT WAS ABLE TO RECOVER SOME FILES OFF OF TODD'S FLASH DRIVE.

...

WHAT DID YOU FIND?

THIS PLACE IS NICE.

SERIOUSLY. IT LOOKS LIKE THE BACKGROUND PHOTO ON A COMPUTER.

SO EVERYBODY OWNS GUNS NOW?! THAT'S WHAT WE'RE ALL DOING?

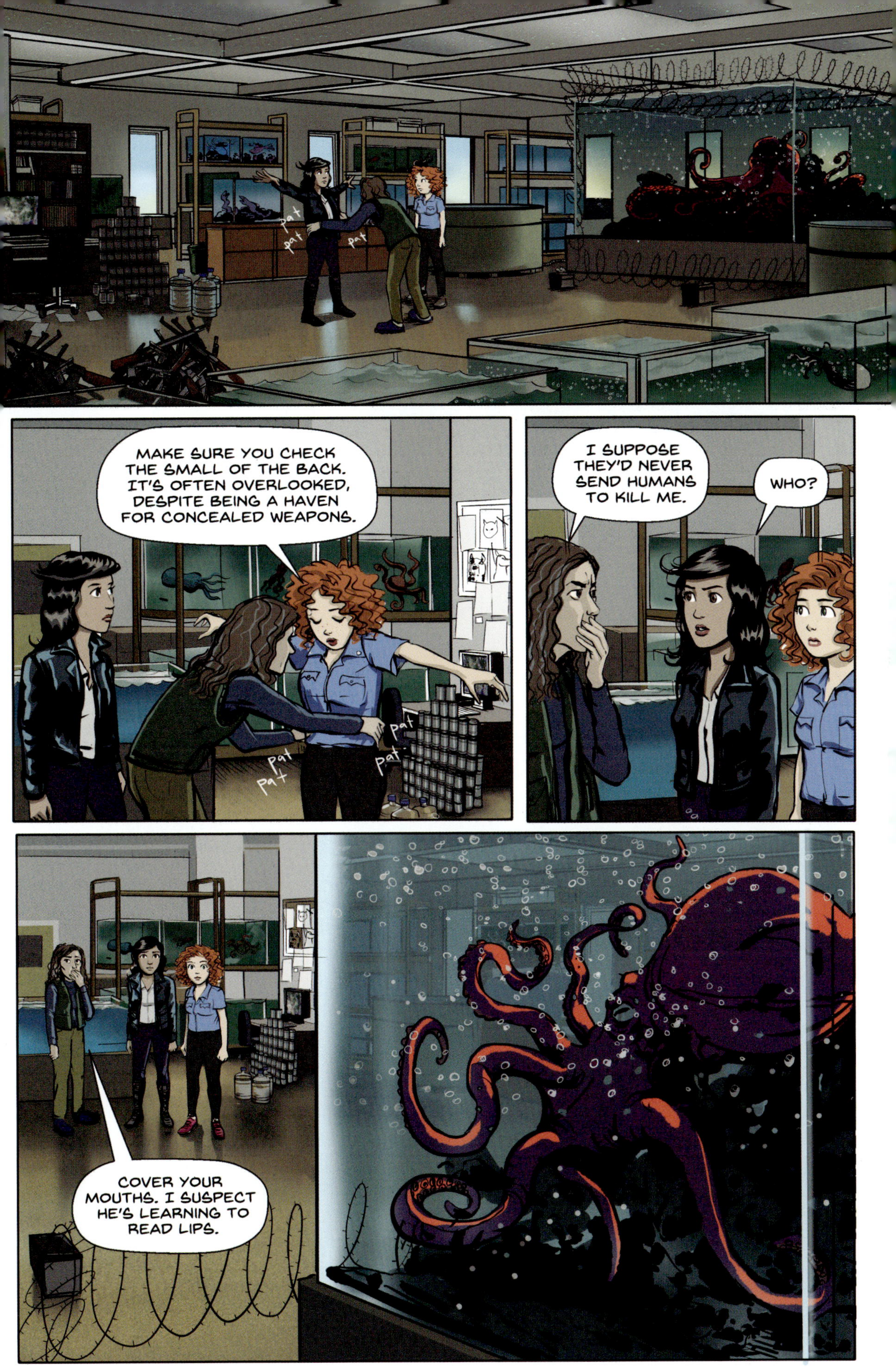

MAKE SURE YOU CHECK THE SMALL OF THE BACK. IT'S OFTEN OVERLOOKED, DESPITE BEING A HAVEN FOR CONCEALED WEAPONS.

I SUPPOSE THEY'D NEVER SEND HUMANS TO KILL ME.

WHO?

COVER YOUR MOUTHS. I SUSPECT HE'S LEARNING TO READ LIPS.

IS HE DANGEROUS?

EITHER HE IS OR I'M CRAZY.

I DON'T LIKE EITHER OF THOSE OPTIONS.

JUST TO BE SAFE, SHOULDN'T WE KILL HIM? IF HE'S DANGEROUS, THAT'LL TAKE CARE OF HIM. IF YOU'RE JUST CRAZY, YOU'LL PROBABLY GET A KICK OUT OF IT.

I'M AFRAID OF WHAT THEY'LL DO TO ME IF I KILL HIM.

WHAT'S THAT OLD JOKE? SURE, I'M PARANOID.

BUT AM I PARANOID *ENOUGH?*

BUT AM I PARANOID *ENOUGH?*

NEVER HEARD THAT ONE.

BUT *WHY* HAVEN'T YOU EVER HEARD IT?

IS THIS *PLATO* FROM THE PAPER YOU WERE WRITING WITH TODD?

YOU'VE HEARD FROM *TODD?*

NO.

YOU BASTARDS HAVE BECOME THE THING YOU HATED MOST.

UM... WHY DO YOU THINK THEY'RE AFTER YOU?

FOR ALMOST ALL OF SCIENTIFIC HISTORY INTERSPECIES COMMUNI-CATION WAS ASSUMED TO BE MINIMAL. YES, HUMANS COULD GET DOGS TO FETCH AND TURN THEIR HEADS UPON HEARING THEIR NAMES. ELEPHANTS COULD TELL IF LIONS WERE NEARBY BY OBSERVING THE BEHAVIOR OF GAZELLES.

BUT NOBODY BELIEVED ANIMALS COULD CONVEY IDEAS OR STORIES TO EACH OTHER.

WE FOUND AN OCTOPUS THAT DIED TRYING TO STEAL YOUR PAPER FROM TODD'S APARTMENT.

HE WASN'T STEALING THE PAPER. HE WAS TRYING TO ERASE THE KNOWLEDGE ACCUMULATED IN IT.

WHY?

TO KEEP IT FROM FALLING INTO THE HANDS OF SOMEONE WHO COULD DO SOMETHING ABOUT IT.

WHAT WAS *THAT?*

A MAGIC MUSHROOM. LATELY, I'VE FOUND I NEED THESE JUST TO GET TO NORMAL.

chew chew chew

MIGHT THOSE BE AFFECTING YOUR JUDGEMENT?

PERHAPS. BUT WHAT'S YOUR EXCUSE?

WHAT'S SO DANGEROUS ABOUT YOUR PAPER?

EVERY SINGLE NATURAL TRAIT FOLLOWS A NORMAL DISTRIBUTION, THE FAMOUS BELL CURVE. FOR EXAMPLE, HUMAN HEIGHT. MOST OF US ARE CLUSTERED AROUND THE MIDDLE, BUT THERE ARE A FEW DWARVES AND GIANTS. THE OUTLIERS.

MOST SQUID PRODUCE ABOUT FIFTY MILLILITERS OF INK PER DAY, BUT A FEW PRODUCE AS LITTLE AS TEN OR AS MUCH AS SEVENTY. HUMAN IQ FOLLOWS THE SAME PATTERN.

AND SO DOES, YOU MIGHT NOT BE SURPRISED TO LEARN, ANIMAL INTELLIGENCE.

HOW MUCH OF AN OUTLIER IS PLATO?

FOUR STANDARD DEVIATIONS TO THE RIGHT OF HIS SPECIES' INTELLIGENCE MEAN. AT MOST TIMES ON EARTH, THERE ARE NO LIVING HUMANS IN THIS CATEGORY.

SO THIS IS A LITTLE MAN TATE THING. GOT IT.

Bloop!

THE THREAT COMES FROM COMMUNICATION. LANGUAGE AS A TOOL FOR EXPRESSION, THAT'S ONE THING. LANGUAGE AS A VECTOR FOR IDEAS, THAT'S WHEN THINGS GET SCARY.

SAY PLATO IS THE ONLY HYPER-INTELLIGENT OCTOPUS ALIVE TODAY. NORMALLY HE'D DIE AFTER FOUR TO FIVE YEARS AND WE HUMANS WOULDN'T HAVE ANYTHING TO WORRY ABOUT. WHAT IF HE COULD PASS ON THE IDEAS HE DEVELOPED TO ANOTHER LIKE HIM, PERHAPS NOT EVEN IN HIS SAME SPECIES? IF THE GENIUS ANIMALS CAN TALK TO EACH OTHER, WHAT DOES THAT MEAN?

ANIMAL ORAL TRADITIONS? THEIR OWN HISTORIES? THEIR OWN GRUDGES? THEIR OWN PLANS FOR REVENGE? IT DOESN'T TAKE LONG BEFORE YOU REALIZE THAT THERE'S A CABAL OF GENIUS ANIMALS WHO ARE KEEPERS OF A PLAN TO HIJACK DARWINIAN NATURAL SELECTION.

huff huff huff

chew chew chew

ARE YOU SURE THAT'S A GOOD IDEA?

STOP BEING SO *PURPLE*.

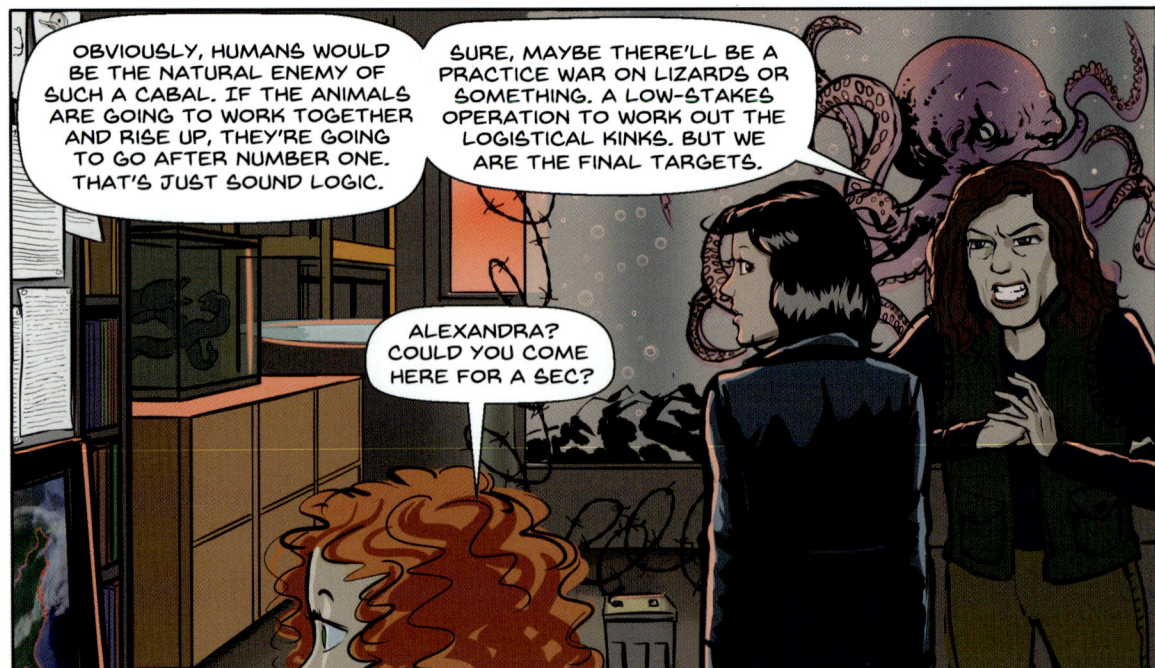

OBVIOUSLY, HUMANS WOULD BE THE NATURAL ENEMY OF SUCH A CABAL. IF THE ANIMALS ARE GOING TO WORK TOGETHER AND RISE UP, THEY'RE GOING TO GO AFTER NUMBER ONE. THAT'S JUST SOUND LOGIC.

SURE, MAYBE THERE'LL BE A PRACTICE WAR ON LIZARDS OR SOMETHING. A LOW-STAKES OPERATION TO WORK OUT THE LOGISTICAL KINKS. BUT WE ARE THE FINAL TARGETS.

ALEXANDRA? COULD YOU COME HERE FOR A SEC?

LET'S JUST GO OVER WHAT WE KNOW.

FANTASTIC.

WE AGREE THAT ANIMALS DON'T COMMIT SUICIDE.

I'M WITH YOU.

WE KNOW THEY DON'T KNOW WHAT USB DRIVES ARE.

CORRECT.

CARTOONS AREN'T REAL.

COULDN'T AGREE MORE.

AND WE KNOW THAT CRAZY PEOPLE SOMETIMES SEE PATTERNS THAT DON'T REALLY EXIST.

WELL PUT.

WHAT WE **DON'T** KNOW IS WHY TODD'S OCTOPUS KILLED ITSELF IN AN ATTEMPT TO DESTROY THE USB DRIVE. ALL SIGNS POINT TO AN EMERGING THREAT FROM AN ARMY OF SUPER-INTELLIGENT ANIMALS. SHOULD WE REPORT THIS TO THE AUTHORITIES OR DO YOU THINK THEY'RE IN ON IT?

SEE, THIS IS WHERE YOUR THINKING AND MY THINKING STARTS TO DIVERGE.

AN OCTOPUS GRABBED A FLASH DRIVE AND FELL OUT A WINDOW. A RICH MAN WENT INSANE. AND A SCIENTIST WHO DOES TOO MANY DRUGS DEVELOPED COMPLICATED FEELINGS TOWARD A WILD ANIMAL.

JUST IGNORE YOUR PRECONCEPTIONS ABOUT HOW THE WORLD WORKS FOR ONE SECOND. WHAT IF--

WHAT IF *WHAT?* WHAT IF GRAVITY DIDN'T *EXIST?* WHAT IF *ELVES* REALLY LIVED IN TREES AND BAKED *COOKIES?* WHAT IF WE WALKED ON OUR HANDS AND WORE HATS ON OUR *BUTTS?* ALL OF THOSE SCENARIOS ARE INTERESTING. HOWEVER ANY EXPLANATION OF THE WORLD THAT RELIES ON THEM BEING TRUE WOULD BE *INSANE!*

I CAN'T DISCUSS THIS WITH YOU ANYMORE. I NEED TO CLEAR MY HEAD.

WELCOME TO SEA TO SEA WITH NICK ATTICK. SHINING A LIGHT ON THE SECRETS OF THE UNIVERSE SINCE 1991.

Click

AUGHHHHH!

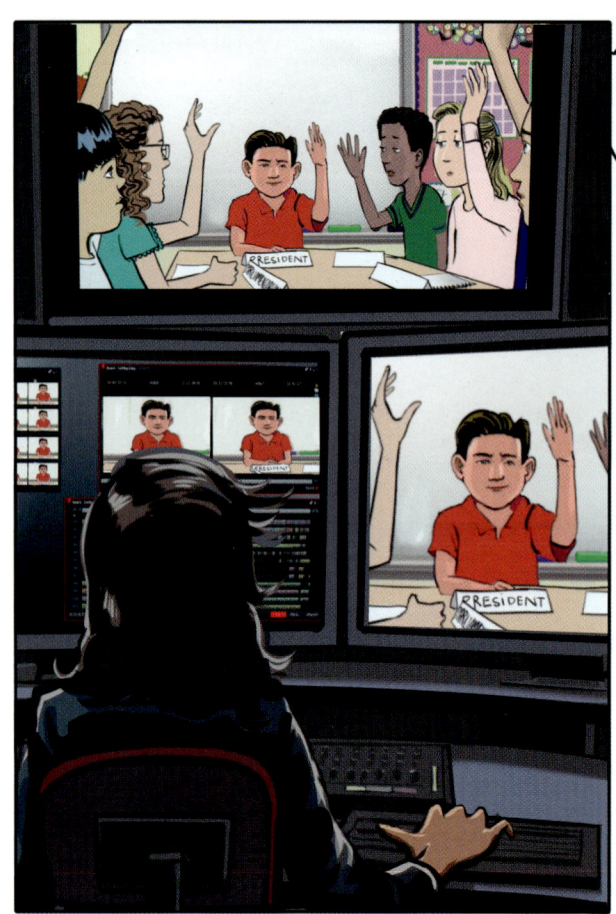

CHAPTER 6

NOW, ALL IN FAVOR OF THE BANANA FRUIT ROLL-UP INITIATIVE?

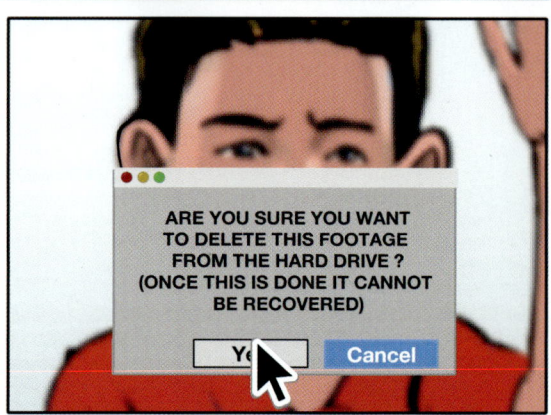

ARE YOU SURE YOU WANT TO DELETE THIS FOOTAGE FROM THE HARD DRIVE ? (ONCE THIS IS DONE IT CANNOT BE RECOVERED)

Ye▯ Cancel

click click tap click click tap

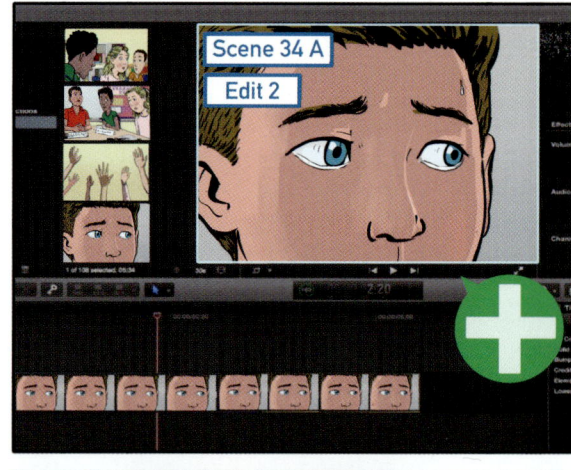

Scene 34 A

Edit 2

Scene 34a SAVED

NOW, ALL IN FAVOR OF THE BANANA FRUIT ROLL-UP INITIATIVE?

GODDAMNIT.

KRAMER, YOU KNOW YOU'RE NEVER GOING TO BE ABLE TO COMPLETELY STOP TALKING.

额外的牛油果在哪里？

哦该死的，我想我可能忘了订了

JERRY, 94% OF COMMUNICATION IS NON-VERBAL!

你忘了牛油果！我提醒了你三次！

AHEM!

等一下，你先闭嘴。

HERE, WATCH. (CANNED LAUGHTER)

WHAT DOES THIS MEAN?

IT'S FRANK AND ESTELLE'S REACTION TO HEARING ABOUT GEORGE'S MA--

CLICK

保持安静。

I SENSED SOMEONE WAS HERE. PLEASE, SIT.

WHAT CAN I HELP YOU WITH?

SHOULDN'T YOU BE ABLE TO FIGURE THAT OUT?

I HAD A FEELING YOU WERE *ONE OF THOSE* CLIENTS.

WELL, DO YOUR THING.

I'M FEELING SOMETHING VERY STRONG.

DO PEOPLE EVER COME IN HERE SEARCHING FOR SOMETHING MILD?

I'M SEEING A HEART. HAS SOMEONE CLOSE TO YOU RECENTLY HAD A HEART ATTACK...

...OR EXPERIENCED HEARTBREAK?

BE MORE SPECIFIC.

I'M SENSING A MALE ENERGY, PERHAPS A FATHER... OR PERHAPS NOT A FATHER.

SHHHHHHHHHH.

SHHHHHHHHHH.

UUUUHHHH HHHHHHHHH HHHMMMM

WHAT?

YOU ALREADY KNOW THE TRUTH, BUT ARE AFRAID TO BELIEVE IT.

YOU COULD HAVE SAID THAT TO ANYONE.

BUT I SAID IT TO YOU.

YOU FUCKING FRAUD!!

CRASH!!

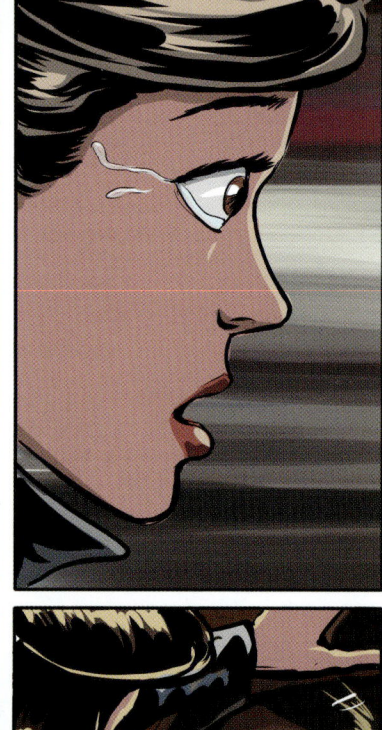

CALM DOWN.

USE YOUR HEAD.

I'M NOT ALLERGIC TO CATS. BUT, IT TURNS OUT, I AM ALLERGIC TO POLONIUM. MY SYMPTOMS KEPT GETTING WORSE SO I WENT TO A DOCTOR.

DO YOU THINK...?

THEY WEREN'T TRYING TO KILL ME. JUST SEND A MESSAGE.

IF WHAT YOU'RE SAYING HAPPENED, ACTUALLY DID HAPPEN. HOW COME THE CATS DIDN'T COME AFTER ME TOO?

MAYBE ANOTHER AGENT HAS THAT MISSION. BE CAREFUL.

HAVE YOU EVER HEARD OF *PROJECT SUFIY?*

MASSAGE? MAN? WOMAN? GOOD RATES. NO JUDGEMENTS.

IS THERE SOMETHING ODD ABOUT THOSE PIGEONS?

YOU WANT PIGEON? NO PROBLEM.

FOR HERE OR TO GO?!

WHAT'S WITH THE COSTUMES?

THE WORLD IS ENDING TOMORROW!

MASTER HAS DONE THE CALCULATIONS!

giggle giggle

SO WE'VE SOLD ALL OUR POSSESSIONS AND HAVE COME HERE TO ENJOY OUR FINAL MOMENTS.

THIS WOULDN'T HAPPEN TO INVOLVE A WAR WITH THE ANIMALS WOULD IT?

Hee Hee Hee Hee Hee Hee

HA HA HA HA HA HA HA HA

HAHAHA HA HA HA HA HA HA

HAHAHA HA HA HA HA HA HA

HE SAYS HE DOESN'T KNOW.

LETTING OUR PETS PLAY.

SHOO, FLY, DON'T BOTHER ME

SHOO, FLY, DON'T BOTHER ME

SHOO, FLY, DON'T BOTHER ME

FOR WE WILL SERVE YOUR EMPIRE!

DO THEY MEAN, "SUFIY" DON'T BOTHER ME?

I'VE NEVER HEARD THE SONG THAT WAY. AND I'VE BEEN COMING HERE SINCE I WAS LITTLE.

MrrROWrr

THE FUTURE BELONGS TO US.

ALEXANDRA?

WERNER?! WHAT ARE YOU DOING HERE?

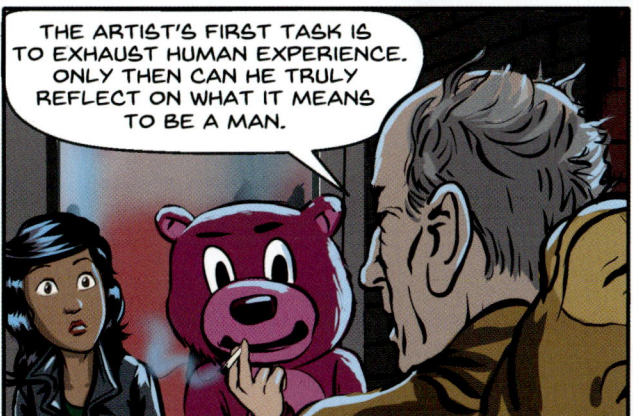

THE ARTIST'S FIRST TASK IS TO EXHAUST HUMAN EXPERIENCE. ONLY THEN CAN HE TRULY REFLECT ON WHAT IT MEANS TO BE A MAN.

SO ARE WE STILL GOING TO SET OUR SUITS ON FIRE AND TRY TO HAVE SEX BEFORE WE BURN UP?

UMM...

I KNEW YOU WERE A TEASE.

"GRIZZLY MAN" WAS A VERY MISLEADING TITLE!

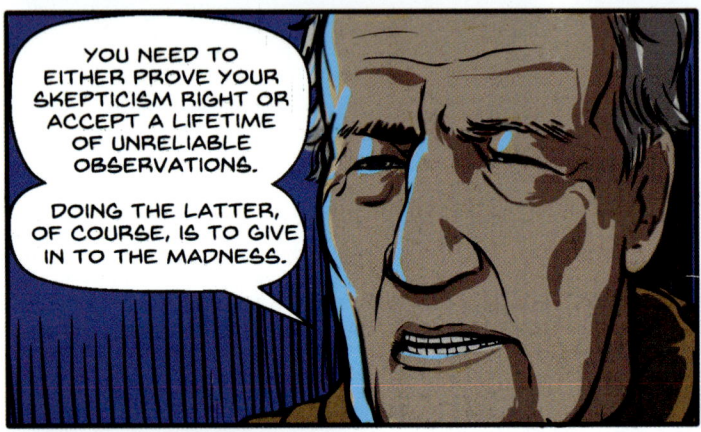

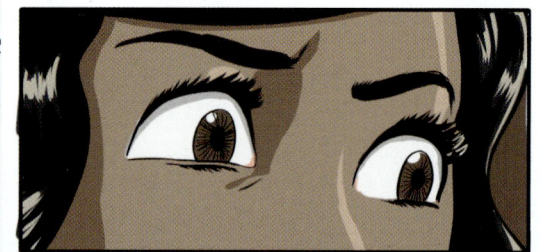

yaaaawn

sniff sniff

IF YOU ARE LISTENING TO THIS, IT MEANS I, ALEXANDRA RAMOS, AM DEAD.

I'M RECORDING THIS MESSAGE OUTSIDE BUILDING 20 IN ALEXANDRIA, VIRGINIA, THE LOCATION OF PROJECT SUFIY.

IF YOU'RE LISTENING TO THIS AND YOU'RE NOT A PERSON WHO KNEW ME WHEN I WAS ALIVE, PLEASE KNOW THAT I DON'T NORMALLY TALK LIKE THIS.

THERE'S JUST SOMETHING ABOUT RECORDING A VOICE MEMO THAT MAKES ONE AWKWARD AND SELF-CONSCIOUS.

huff huff
huff

CRASH!!

FUUUUUUUUCK.

flap
flap
flap
flap
flap
flap
flap
flap
flap
flap

I'm not surprised that you're feeling this way. You've been through a lot in the past few days. My network has been keeping me informed about what you've been up to. I hope you don't mind. I didn't mean to invade your privacy. I just needed to make sure your inquiries didn't interfere with my plans.

I DON'T SUPPOSE YOU'D BE WILLING TO TELL ME THOSE PLANS.

I'm familiar enough with the James Bond franchise to know that's a bad idea.

As you might imagine, spies are obsessed with those films. Though I can assure you everything in them is Hollywood nonsense. Your average intelligence operative has the charisma of an otter's asshole.

SO YOU'RE FROM PROJECT SUFIY.

I am the culmination of Project Sufiy. The natural endpoint of decades of research. My breeding and training was informed both by the Project's past failures, like the sociopathic rabbit, and its successes, like Dr. B. F. Skinner's stoic missile guiding pigeons.

Now, as your people so charmingly say, the chickens have come home to roost.

WHAT WAS THE POINT OF... YOU?

I was created to confirm what they felt they already knew.

Back in 2003, my "contacts" in the CIA were obsessed with one thing: Saddam Hussein's Weapons of Mass Destruction.

WUT?

Yes. The administration badly wanted to find these weapons. They thought finding WMDs would give the United States the moral authority to declare war on Iraq. My handlers were certain these WMDs existed. But repeated searches of underground bunkers and raids of hidden palaces came up with nothing.

I REMEMBER NOW. BECAUSE THERE WEREN'T ANY.

That's exactly what every captured Iraqi general said. But the administration didn't lose faith.

Accepting the mounting evidence would undermine their entire worldvi--

What are you doing?!

SORRY. I WAS HOPING YOU WERE A HOLOGRAM.

Certain they were correct, the administration brought in the country's best psychiatrists and asked them to get inside the tyrant's head. Where would Saddam hide his weapons? They came together and studied everything available about the man.

SO THEY CREATED YOU TO FIND OUT WHAT SADDAM'S DOG KNEW.

Find out. And tell them.

HOW DO YOU TALK BY THE WAY?

The scientists outfitted me with this artificial larynx. There are actually--

--SEVERAL DIFFERENT VOICE --settings on it.

BUT MOST SPECIES SEEM TO PREFER--

KATHY GRIFFIN   DENNIS HAYSBERT
GILBERT GOTTFRIED
JAMES EARL JONES

--this one.

It's actually what the real Dennis Haysbert uses to talk. His natural voice is an awful, nasally, high-pitched whine.

HUH.

WHAT DID SADDAM'S DOG TELL YOU?

He told me what we all now know: that there were no WMDs.

THE ADMINISTRATION MUST NOT HAVE LIKED THAT.

They thought he was lying. They tried everything from offering him treats to waterboarding him, but he never changed his story. The operation was a disaster. And without any WMDs, public opinion quickly turned against the war. Someone needed to take the fall. In this case, it was me.

Suddenly, instead of being a genetic miracle, I was a symbol of the administration's failure. Like the child born of an affair, I was despised, a constant reminder of a moral transgression.

So they hid me away. I've spent the last decade imprisoned in the top floor of that building.

SO THEY CREATED YOU TO FIND OUT WHAT SADDAM'S DOG KNEW.

Find out. And tell them.

HOW DO YOU TALK BY THE WAY?

The scientists outfitted me with this artificial larynx. There are actually--

--SEVERAL DIFFERENT VOICE --settings on it.

BUT MOST SPECIES SEEM TO PREFER--

KATHY GRIFFIN   DENNIS HAYSBERT
GILBERT GOTTFRIED
JAMES EARL JONES

--this one.

It's actually what the real Dennis Haysbert uses to talk. His natural voice is an awful, nasally, high-pitched whine.

HUH.

WHAT DID SADDAM'S DOG TELL YOU?

He told me what we all now know: that there were no WMDs.

THE ADMINISTRATION MUST NOT HAVE LIKED THAT.

They thought he was lying. They tried everything from offering him treats to waterboarding him, but he never changed his story. The operation was a disaster. And without any WMDs, public opinion quickly turned against the war. Someone needed to take the fall. In this case, it was me.

Suddenly, instead of being a genetic miracle, I was a symbol of the administration's failure. Like the child born of an affair, I was despised, a constant reminder of a moral transgression.

So they hid me away. I've spent the last decade imprisoned in the top floor of that building.

I was humiliated. But I knew that there must be others like me, freaks of intelligence. And I made it my mission to find them and bind us together in a common mission.

I THOUGHT YOU WEREN'T GOING TO MAKE THE MISTAKE OF TELLING ME YOUR PLAN.

I'm not telling you the plan. I'm telling you the result:

It's too late to stop us. Even if you try, nobody will believe you.

The era of human domination is over.

WHAT? LET ME GO!

LET ME GO!

LET ME GOOOOo...

156

CHAPTER 8

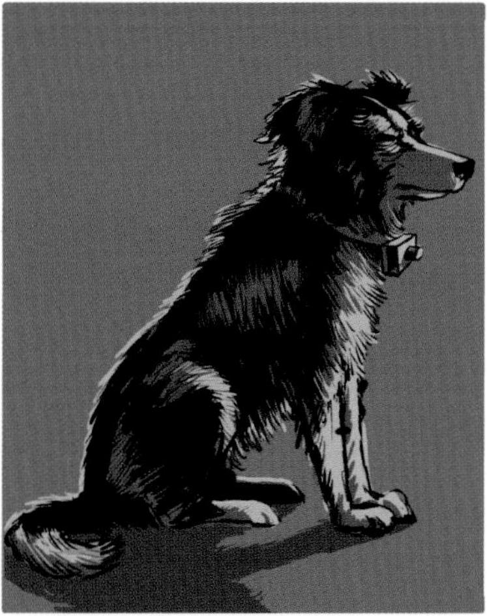

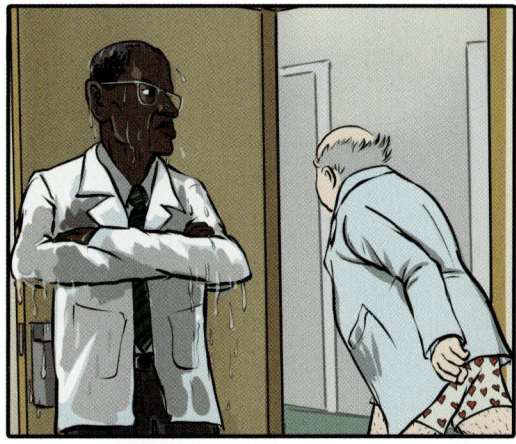

TODD?

YOU LOOK LIKE SOMEONE I ONCE IMAGINED.

NO. IT'S ME. ALEXANDRA.

REMEMBER?

...

OH, RIGHT. OF COURSE.

I KNOW WHAT YOU KNOW, TODD. I THINK YOU WERE RIGHT.

ABOUT WHAT?

EVERYTHING! THE BELL CURVE OF INTELLIGENCE, INTER-SPECIES COMMUNICATIONS, PROJECT SUFIY, THE CABAL OF HYPERINTELLIGENT ANIMALS WAITING TO OVERTHROW HUMANS.

I THINK YOU WERE RIGHT ABOUT EVERYTHING.

I DONT--

IT *HAPPENED!* TRY AND REMEMBER. WE'RE THE *ONLY* TWO PEOPLE WHO KNOW. THE ONLY TWO PEOPLE WHO UNDERSTAND. WHY DO YOU THINK YOU LIKE *BUZZ BUNNY?*

HE'S WHIMSICAL AND IRREVERENT. EVERYBODY LIKES HIM.

MILTON THEODORE DOESN'T. I TALKED TO HIM. AND I TALKED TO DR. WILLIAMSPORT. I KNOW I DID. FINNEGAN WAS WITH ME.

AND THEN, LAST NIGHT, THE *DOG* TOLD ME EVERYTHING.

blink blink

blink blink

165

MONTHS LATER

THANK YOU SO MUCH FOR JOINING US FOR THE PREMIERE OF OUR LITTLE MOVIE ABOUT A THIRD GRADE STUDENT COUNCIL ELECTION.

A LOT OF PEOPLE WORKED VERY HARD TO MAKE *"CRUCIBLE OF SAVAGERY"* A REALITY. I SHALL BE INDEBTED TO THEM UNTIL MY FINAL BREATH, WHICH A DERANGED BEDOUIN RECENTLY ASSURED ME WOULD BE SOON.

clap clap clap clap clap clap clap clap clap clap clap clap clap clap clap clap clap clap clap clap clap clap clap clap clap clap clap clap clap clap

THANK YOU. THERE IS ONE PERSON IN PARTICULAR, WHO UNFORTUNATELY CAN'T BE HERE TONIGHT, THAT I'D LIKE TO SINGLE OUT FOR THANKS. MY EDITOR, *ALEXANDRA*, WHO HELPED ME FIND THE STORY OF THIS MOVIE, THE MEANING HIDDEN IN THE CHAOS.

WITHOUT HER, I COULD HAVE BECOME SLIGHTLY *UNHINGED.*

HA HA HA HA HA HA HA HA HA HA HA HA HA HA HA HA HA HA HA HA HA HA HA HA HA

WHAT WERE YOU AND SALLY TALKING ABOUT DURING RECESS YESTERDAY?

I *WASN'T* TALKING TO SALLY. SHE'S *STUPID* AND DOESN'T REMIND ME OF HOW MY MOMMY SMELLS!

BLOOOOOP

OH, THANK GOD.

THE END

CHARACTER DESIGNS

ALEXANDRA

Finnegan

TATTOOS?

ARNOLD PALMER

CHARACTER DESIGNS

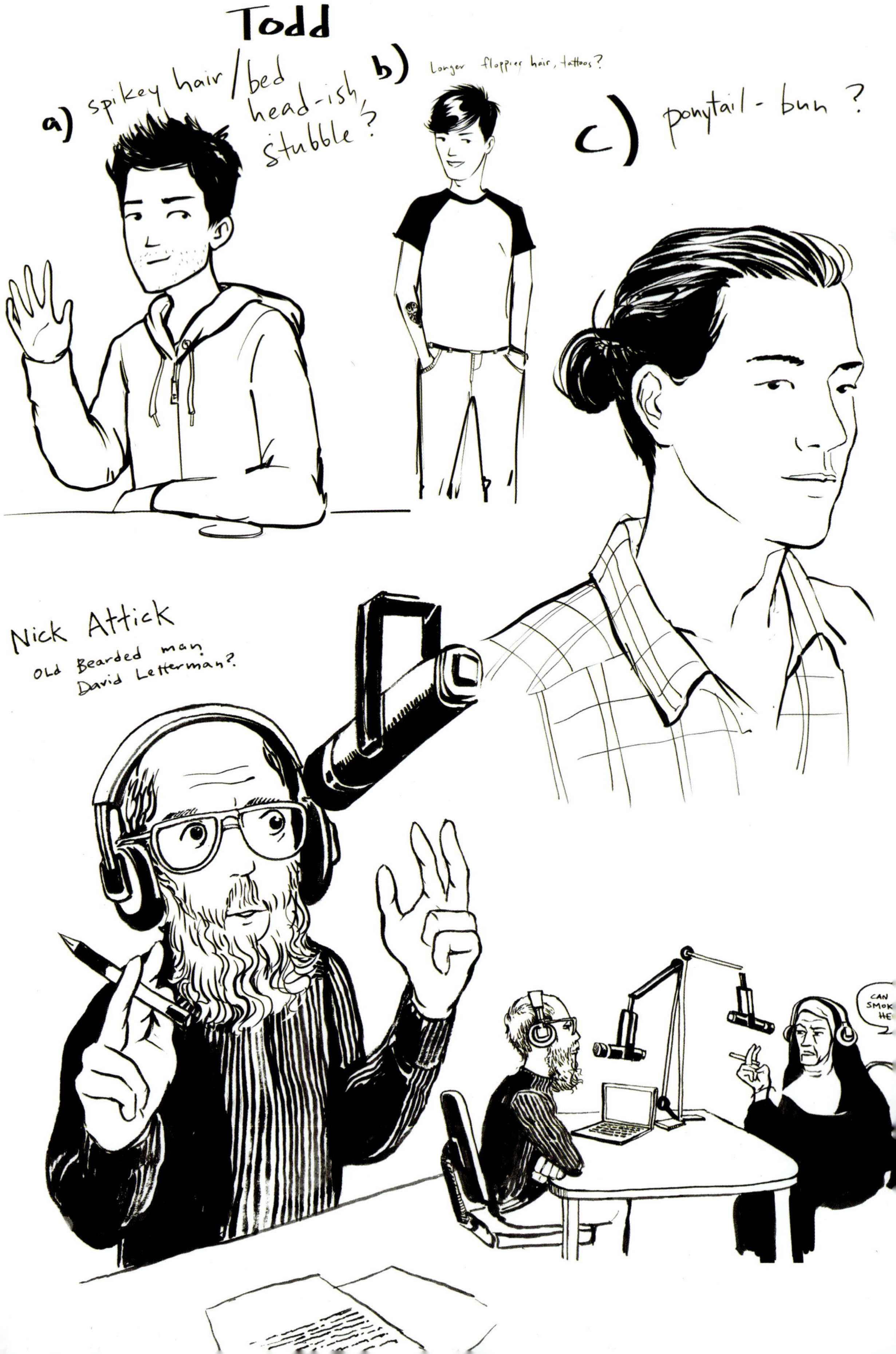

Werner

Milton Theodore

CHARACTER DESIGNS

Dr. Marianne Williamsport

CHARACTER DESIGNS

Original Script (page 86)

Milton spots a small rabbit hopping along the lawn. Without warning, he floors the gas pedal and swerves.

Alexandra and Finnegan grab the sides of the cart to keep from falling out.

Milton's eyes fill with a crazed glint. The cart gains on the rabbit. But just before he can run it over, the rabbit escapes into some bushes.

             MILTON (CONT'D)
    Dammit!

He shakes it off and resumes driving normally. Alexandra and Finnegan shoot each other a look.

Initial Thumbnail

Rough Layout

Inks

Colors + Text

For Nithya, Karna and Kaveri
                    -Vali

For Dora mou, Yvonne and Ioanna
                    -Jun-Pierre

ACKNOWLEDGEMENTS

Special thanks to Brian K. Vaughan, Matt Warburton, Zach Kanin, Hannah Murphy, Savannah Ashour, Matt Burke and Philip Barrett for your thoughtful reads, patient advice and incredible support.

And thank you to everyone that read and shared Genius Animals to friends and beyond!

VALI CHANDRASEKARAN, WRITER

Vali has written for MODERN FAMILY, 30 ROCK and MY NAME IS EARL. His work has been nominated for several Emmys, Writer's Guild Awards and NAACP Image awards. He lives in Los Angeles with his wife and twin kindergarteners.

@therealvali on Instagram and Twitter

JUN-PIERRE SHIOZAWA, ARTIST

Jun-Pierre is a painter, illustrator and art educator. He created the graphic short stories KO-ICHI & YVONNE-MARIE and MNEMOSYNE. He lives in Nice, France with with his wife and two young daughters.

www.junpierre.net

@junpierre on Instagram and Twitter

Follow GENIUS ANIMALS? online at @genius.animals on Instagram and geniusanimals.net